Jack And The French Languasaurus

Fruit

One cold Saturday morning Jack was coming out of the local supermarket when he saw an old lady's shopping bag break and all her shopping fall onto the floor. Jack quickly rushed over to help.

The old lady must have been French as she said "**merci**" and that means thank you in French. She then slipped an usual looking coin in Jack's hand as she left.

Jack liked learning French at school. He also loved dinosaurs!
Back home in his garden Jack was thinking about both of these
things when he dropped the unusual coin he had been given.

Jack had learnt that the French say "**Oh la la**" when they are
surprised, and he loved saying this whenever he was surprised.
And today he was *certainly* surprised.   When he dropped the coin
un oeuf appeared. That's an egg! And it was rather big!

Suddenly the egg cracked and out of the egg popped……………… a French languasaurus!

The magic coin had created the languasaurus because Jack was thinking about both French and dinosaurs when he had dropped it!

The languasaurus said "**Bonjour**" as he spoke French, and that's how the French say hello.

Jack said hello and introduced himself in French.

The languasaurus then said "**J'ai faim**". At first,
Jack didn't understand what the languasaurus was
saying. But then when he started rubbing his tummy
Jack realised that he must be hungry. So he went away to get
something for him to eat.

But what would a languasaurus eat? He'd read that many
dinosaurs ate plants so Jack went into the kitchen to see what he
could find.

He soon returned with some fruit. He wasn't sure if the languasaurus would like fruit, but there was only one way to find out!

The languasaurus jumped on a box as he said "merci". That's thank you in French.

The languasaurus was very hungry but he wanted to teach Jack how to say a banana in French. So, before he ate a banana he said "**une banane**".

Jack didn't know the French word for a banana, so he repeated "**une banane**."

Next the languasaurus wanted to teach Jack how to say an apple in French.

The languasaurus told Jack to clap twice as they said together **une pomme**. They did this three times:

"**Une pomme, une pomme, une pomme**."

(If you are reading this story now join in too!)

So an apple in French was **une pomme**.

And then the languasaurus wanted to teach Jack how to say a pear in French.

The languasaurus told Jack to clap twice as they said together **une poire**. They did this three times:

"**Une poire, une poire, une poire**."

(If you are reading this story now join in too!)

So a pear in French was **une poire**.

And finally the languasaurus wanted to teach Jack how to say an orange in French.

The languasaurus told Jack to clap three times as they said together **une orange**. They did this three times:

"**Une orange, une orange, une orange.**"

(If you are reading this story now join in too!)

So an orange in French was **une orange**.

It was soon time for a game. The languasaurus put down three fruit in front of Jack, and they said together the names of the fruit in French as they clapped.

(If you are reading this book now try saying each French word twice as you clap. It's fun to do!)

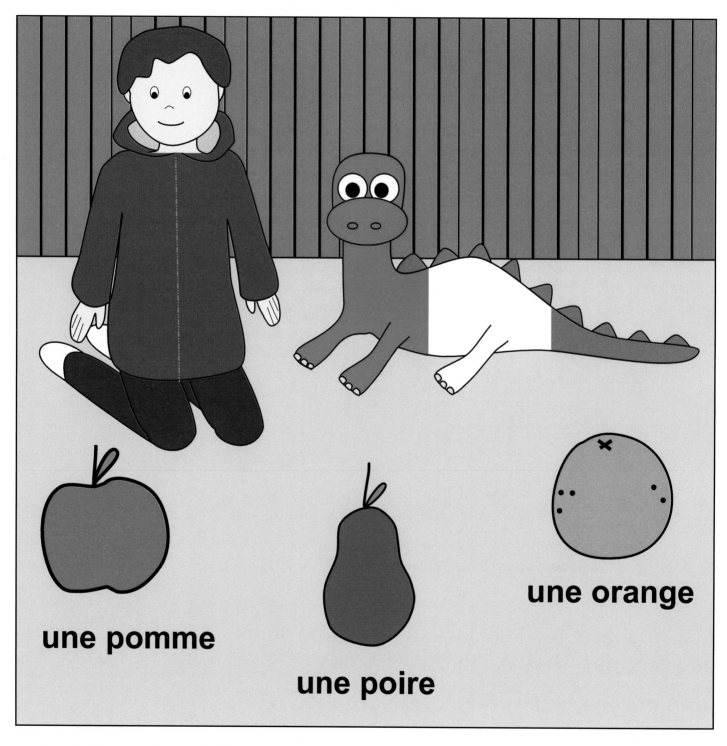

une pomme

une poire

une orange

Jack then closed his eyes and the languasaurus took one away.

The languasaurus wanted to know which one was missing?

Une pomme?   Une poire?   Une orange?

Can YOU work out which one is missing?

The missing fruit was **une pomme**!

Jack had learnt the French words for four different types of fruit. Let's say them together in French:

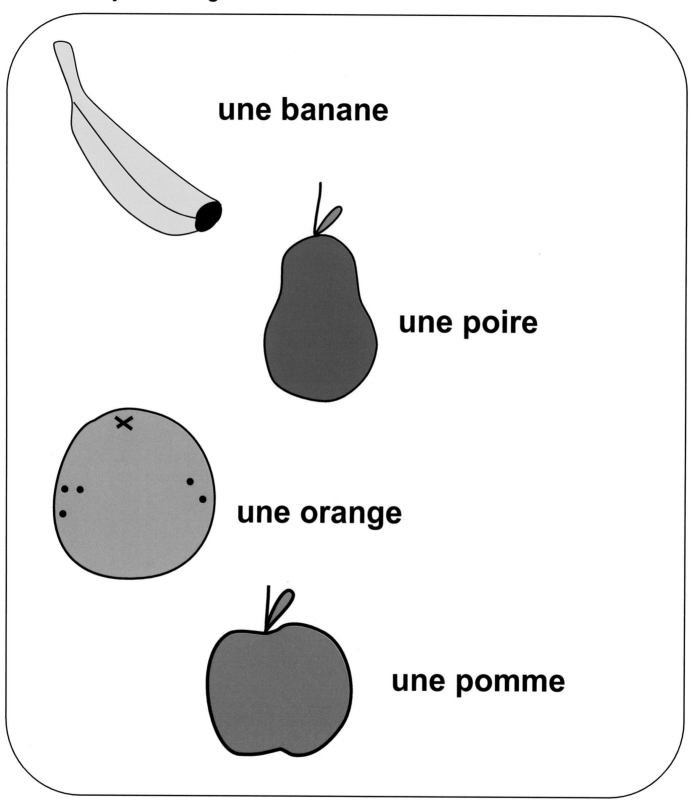

une banane

une poire

une orange

une pomme

It was nearly dinner time, so Jack and the French languasaurus said "**Au revoir**" as that's how the French say goodbye. Jack then skipped happily back inside. It had been such a fun afternoon!

Jack And The French Languasaurus

The Missing Sheep

Sunday morning Jack woke up a bit earlier than usual. He was very keen to see how the languasaurus was.

Jack asked in French how the languasaurus was, and the languasaurus replied "**Ça va très bien.**" That means he was very good.

Jack lived with his parents on a lovely farm. Jack decided to show the languasaurus the wonderful sheep they had on the farm.

The languasaurus told Jack that in French sheep are **les moutons**.

They then counted **les moutons** together in French:

Un deux trois quatre cinq six.

Il y a six moutons. (There are six sheep)

The next day Jack heard his parents talking about the sheep. He was worried that there may be something wrong, so he wanted to go and see if they were okay. The languasaurus was fast asleep, so Jack had to wake him by saying loudly "**Bonjour !**"

They hurried quickly to see **les moutons**.

They counted **les moutons** in French:

Un deux trois quatre cinq.

Il y a cinq moutons. (There are five sheep)

Jack couldn't believe that there were only five sheep.

"We MUST have miscounted them!" thought Jack.
So they counted them again as normally there are six.

Un deux trois quatre cinq. There were still only five sheep.

The next day Jack wondered if the missing sheep
had returned. So they went back to count the sheep.

They counted **les moutons** in French:

Un deux trois quatre.

Il y a quatre moutons. (There are four sheep)

Jack couldn't believe that there were now only four sheep.

"We MUST have miscounted them!" thought Jack.
So they counted them again. "**Un deux trois quatre**."
There were definitely only four sheep.

The next day Jack wondered if there were any more
sheep missing. So they went back to count the sheep.

They counted **les moutons** in French: Un deux trois.

Il y a trois moutons. There were three sheep.

But there was something else in the field!

un chien

The languasaurus jumped into Jack's arms when he saw a dog run across the field. In French a dog is **un chien**.

"The dog must be there to protect the sheep. The sheep are now safe!" thought Jack.   But the following day Jack wanted to check no more sheep had disappeared.

The next day they counted **les moutons** in French: Un, deux.

Il y a deux moutons et un chien. There are two sheep and a dog! Another sheep was missing! The languasaurus realised it was up to him to solve the mystery of the disappearing sheep.

That night the languasaurus watched the field and he saw a man put **un mouton** (a sheep) in his truck! **Le chien** (the dog) was fast asleep!

The languasaurus jumped on top of the van to see where it went. The truck went to a farm three miles away! The languasaurus then called the police and told them where the stolen sheep were.

The following day, Jack couldn't believe his eyes when he went to count the sheep!

Un deux trois quatre cinq six.

Il y a six moutons! There are six sheep!

The missing sheep had been returned! Jack was very happy!

Useful French words and phrases

Bonjour - - - - - - - - - - - - - - Hello

Je m'appelle Jack - - - - - - - My name is Jack

Comment ça va? - - - - - - - How are you?

Ça va très bien - - - - - - - - Very good

J'ai faim - - - - - - - - - - - - - I am hungry

Merci - - - - - - - - - - - - - - - Thank you

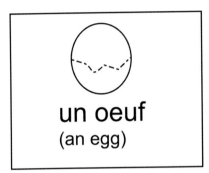
un oeuf
(an egg)

fruit
(fruit)

une banane
(a banana)

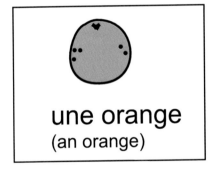
une orange
(an orange)

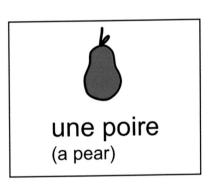
une poire
(a pear)

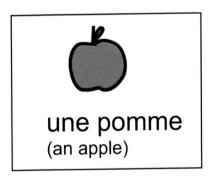
une pomme
(an apple)

un mouton
(a sheep)

un chien
(a dog)

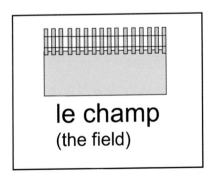
le champ
(the field)

1 un (one) **2** deux (two) **3** trois (three) **4** quatre (four) **5** cinq (five) **6** six (six)

Let's sing a song!

The following words could either be sung to a made up tune, or you could try saying the words as a rap.

For inspiration of a melody to use you could hum first a nursery rhyme. How many different versions can you create using the lyrics?

Un deux trois, un deux trois

Quatre cinq six, quatre cinq six

Il y a six moutons, il y a six moutons

Dans le champ, dans le champ

il y a = there is/are   six moutons = six sheep   dans le champ = in the field

Follow on activity Take 4 pieces of paper, and on each write one of the French words for a fruit and draw a picture.

 une orange   **une poire**   **une pomme**   **une banane**

With at least one other person, take turns to take one of the fruit away. The other person / people have to remember which one is missing.